Contents

Step 1	**Two-digit ÷ one-digit** no carrying	4
Step 2	**Three-digit ÷ one-digit** no carrying	6
Step 3	**Two-digit ÷ one-digit** carrying 1 ten	8
Step 4	**Two-digit ÷ one-digit** carrying several tens	10
Step 5	**Three-digit ÷ one-digit** carrying once	12
Check-up test 1	**Two- and three-digit ÷ one-digit, with carrying**	**14**
Step 6	**Three-digit ÷ one-digit** first digit smaller than the divisor	16
Step 7	**Three-digit ÷ one-digit** carrying tens	18
Step 8	**Three-digit ÷ one-digit** second digit smaller than the divisor	20
Step 9	**Four-digit ÷ one-digit** carrying once, any position	22
Check-up test 2	**Three- and four-digit ÷ one-digit, carrying once**	**24**
Step 10	**Three-digit ÷ one-digit** carrying twice	26
Step 11	**Four-digit ÷ one-digit** carrying two or three times	28
Step 12	**Three- or four-digit ÷ one-digit** answers with remainders	30
Step 13	**Five-digit ÷ one-digit** answers with or without remainders	32
Check-up test 3	**Three-, four- and five-digit ÷ one-digit, carrying more than once and remainders**	**34**
Step 14	**Four-digit ÷ one-digit** with fraction remainders	36
Step 15	**Four-digit ÷ one-digit** with remainders as decimals, 1 dp	38
Step 16	**Four-digit ÷ one-digit** with remainders as decimals, 2 or 3 dp	40
Step 17	**Three-digit ÷ one-digit** with remainders as recurring decimals	42
Step 18	**Dividing decimals by one-digit numbers**	44
Final test	**Whole numbers or decimals ÷ one-digit, with remainders**	**46**

Step I: Two-digit ÷ one-digit no carrying

Written division is different from other written methods as you work from left to right. It is also different as you end up writing the answer on **top** of the question rather than underneath it!

To divide 69 by 3, set it out like this with space for the answer above. ⟶

$$69 \div 3 =$$

What to do

$$69 \div 3 = ?$$

1   Look at the tens digit of the large number. Here it is 6. Divide this digit by the **divisor** (that is, the number you are dividing by) which is 3 here. Ask: *How many 3s in 6?* Write the answer 2 above the line in the tens column.

2   Now look at the units digit of the large number. Here it is 9. Divide this digit by the divisor, 3. Ask: *How many 3s in 9?* Write the answer 3 above the line in the units column to complete the answer.

3   Check that the answer on the top looks about right. You can multiply the answer by the divisor to see if it gives the other number. For example, here 23 × 3 is about 20 × 3 which is 60, so the answer 23 seems about right.

$$69 \div 3 = 23$$

Now you try

I

2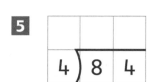

3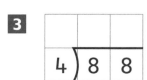

4 3) 6 6

5 4) 8 4

6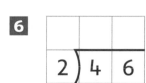

More practice

et out these questions yourself to answer them.

7 $63 \div 3 = ?$

8 $82 \div 2 = ?$

9 $99 \div 3 = ?$

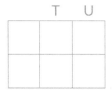

ere you will need to draw the horizontal and vertical lines too!

10 $48 \div 4 = ?$ _____

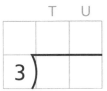

11 $64 \div 2 = ?$ _____

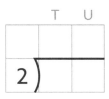

12 $93 \div 3 = ?$ _____

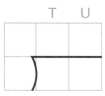

Problem solving

3 Divide 84 by 2.

4 Jo buys three identical chocolate bars.
She paid 96p. How much did each bar cost?

5 Share £62 equally between two people.
How much does each person get?

6 There are 66 sweets altogether in two bags.
Each bag has the same number of sweets.
How many sweets are in each bag?

How did I find Step I? ☐ Easy ☐ OK ☐ Difficult

Step 2: Three-digit ÷ one-digit no carrying

Larger numbers can be divided in the same way as in Step 1. Remember to work from left to right and write the answer on **top** of the question.

$$693 \div 3 =$$

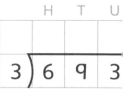

What to do

$$693 \div 3 = ?$$

1 Start with the hundreds digit of the large number. Here it is 6. Divide this digit by the divisor (that is, the number you are dividing by) which is 3 here. Ask: *How many 3s in 6?* Write the answer 2 above the line in the hundreds column.

2 Then look at the tens digit. Here it is 9. Divide this digit by the divisor, 3. Ask: *How many 3s in 9?* Write the answer 3 above the line in the tens column.

3 Now look at the units digit of the large number. Here it is 3. Divide this digit by the divisor, 3. Ask: *How many 3s in 3?* Write the answer 1 above the line in the units column to complete the answer.

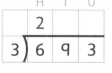

$$693 \div 3 = 231$$

Now you try

1

```
    3
2) 6  4  8
```

2

```
    3
3) 9  9  6
```

Remember that zero divided by a number is zero, for example $0 \div 3 = 0$.

3

```
    2
4) 8  4  4
```

4

```
2) 8  0  6
```

5

```
3) 6  0  9
```

6

```
4) 4  8  8
```

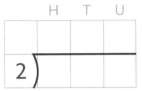 **More practice**   Set out these questions yourself to answer them.

1 $284 \div 2 = ?$

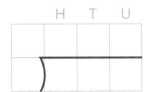

8 $963 \div 3 = ?$

ere you will need to draw the horizontal and vertical lines too!

1 $804 \div 4 = ?$ _____

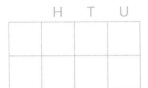

10 $686 \div 2 = ?$ _____

Problem solving

1 Share £699 equally between three people.

_____

2 484 divided by 4 is 121. True or false?

_____

3 If 666 eggs are put into boxes of six, how many boxes are needed?

_____

4 How many more is $428 \div 2$ than $633 \div 3$?

_____

How did I find Step 2?   ☐ Easy   ☐ OK   ☐ Difficult

Step 3: Two-digit ÷ one-digit carrying I ten

In these questions, the tens digit in the number you are dividing is
not a multiple of the divisor (that is, the number you are dividing by).
Notice here that the tens digit, 7, is not a multiple of the divisor, 3.

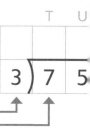

What to do

$75 \div 3 = ?$

I Look at the tens digit of the large number. Here it is 7. Divide this
digit by the divisor, 3. Ask: *How many 3s in 7?* The answer to this
question is 2 remainder I. So write the 2 above the line in the
tens column. Carry the I ten and write it next to the units digit
of the number.

2 Now look in the units column. Instead of 5 units there are now
15 units to divide by 3. Ask: *How many 3s in 15?* Write the answer
5 above the line in the units column to complete the answer.

3 Check that the answer on the top looks about right. You can
multiply the answer by the divisor to see if it gives the other
number. 25 × 3 = 75. Yes, it does.

$75 \div 3 = 25$

Now you try

I
```
        |
   3) 4  '8
```

2
```
       4
   2) 9  '2
```

3
```
       2
   4) 9   6
```

4
```
       2
   3) 7   2
```

5
```
   5) 6   5
```

6
```
   4) 5   2
```

7

8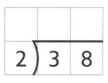

9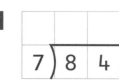

More practice

et out these questions yourself to answer them.

10 45 ÷ 3 = ?

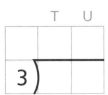

11 74 ÷ 2 = ?

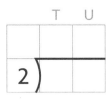

12 78 ÷ 6 = ?

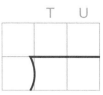

Here you will need to draw the horizontal and vertical lines too!

13 56 ÷ 4 = ? _____

14 58 ÷ 2 = ? _____

15 92 ÷ 4 = ? _____

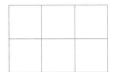   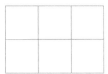   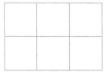

Problem solving

16 Divide 78 by 3.

_____

17 42 children get into groups of three. How many groups of three are there?

_____

18 Share £72 between six people. They each get the same. How much does each get?

_____

19 94 children are asked to line up in two equal rows. How many children will be in each row?

_____

How did I find Step 3?   ☐ Easy   ☐ OK   ☐ Difficult

Step 4: Two-digit ÷ one-digit carrying several tens

In this step, when you divide the first digit, the number you carry may not be 1. It could be 2, 3, 4 or more.

$$68 \div 4 = \text{?}$$

What to do

1   Start with the tens digit. Here it is 6. Divide this digit by the divisor, 4. Ask: *How many 4s in 6?* $6 \div 4 = 1$ remainder 2. So write the answer 1 above the line in the tens column and carry the 2 tens. Write this next to the units digit of the number.

2   Now look in the units column. Instead of 8 units there are now 28 units to divide by 4. Ask: *How many 4s in 28?* Write the answer 7 above the line in the units column to complete the answer.

3   Check that the answer looks about right or multiply the answer by the divisor to see if it gives the other number.

$$68 \div 4 = 17$$

Now you try

1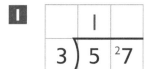

2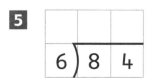

3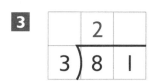

4
5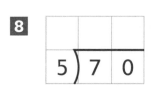

6

7
8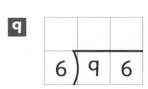

9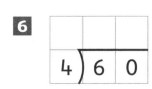

More practice

Set out these questions yourself to answer them.

10 84 ÷ 3 = ?

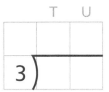

11 91 ÷ 7 = ?

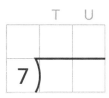

12 85 ÷ 5 = ?

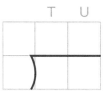

Here you will need to draw the horizontal and vertical lines too!

13 76 ÷ 4 = ? _____

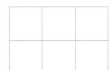

14 95 ÷ 5 = ? _____

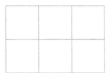

15 54 ÷ 3 = ? _____

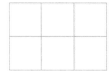

Problem solving

16 Divide 87 by 3.

_____

17 Some sheep are in a field. There are 64 legs in total. How many sheep are there?

_____

18 A gardener is planting 51 trees. He plants three in each row. How many rows of trees does he plant?

_____

19 Chocolate bars are put into packs of five. How many packs of five can be made from 80 bars?

_____

| **How did I find Step 4?** | ☐ Easy | ☐ OK | ☐ Difficult |

Step 5: Three-digit ÷ one-digit carrying once

Larger numbers can be divided in the same way. Remember to work from left to right and to carry a digit across where you need to.

A short way to write 'remainder' is 'r'. So, in the calculation below, instead of writing 'remainder 2', we can write 'r2'.

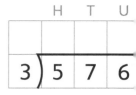

What to do

$576 ÷ 3 = ?$

1   Start with the hundreds digit of the large number. Here it is 5. Divide this digit by the divisor, 3. Ask: *How many 3s in 5?* $5 ÷ 3 = 1$ r2. So write the 1 above the line in the hundreds column and carry the 2 next to the tens digit of the number.

2   Then look at the tens. Instead of 7 tens, there are now 27 tens. Divide 27 by the divisor, 3. Ask: *How many 3s in 27?* $27 ÷ 3 = 9$. Write the answer 9 above the line in the tens column.

3   Now look at the units digit of the number. Here it is 6. Divide this digit by the divisor, 3. Ask: *How many 3s in 6?* Write the answer 2 above the line in the units column to complete the answer.

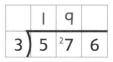

$576 ÷ 3 = 192$

Now you try

1

2

3
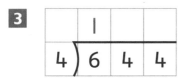

4
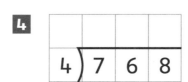

5
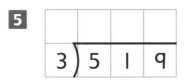

6
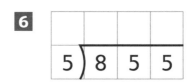

More practice

et out these questions yourself to answer them.

7 426 ÷ 3 = ?

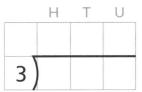

8 726 ÷ 6 = ?

or these questions remember that zero divided by a number is zero, for example 0 ÷ 3 = 0.

9

3) 8 1 0

10

8) 9 6 0

Problem solving

11 546 ÷ 3 has the same answer as 364 ÷ 2. True or false?

_____

12 655 ÷ 5 has the same answer as 786 ÷ 6. True or false?

_____

13 910 ÷ 7 has the same answer as 520 ÷ 4. True or false?

_____

14 Mrs Pot buys 489 teabags. She uses three teabags each day. How many days will the teabags last?

_____

How did I find Step 5?   ☐ Easy   ☐ OK   ☐ Difficult

Check-up test 1 Two- and three-digit ÷ one-digit, with carrying

Step 1

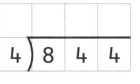

2

3 $84 \div 4 = ?$

Step 2

4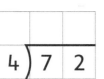

5 $963 \div 3 = ?$

Step 3

6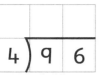

7 $45 \div 3 = ?$

Step 4

8

9 $85 \div 5 = ?$ _____

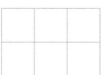

Step 5

10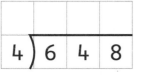

11 $655 \div 5 = ?$ _____

Steps 1 to 5 mixed

Use the grid below for working.

2 Share 96p between three people. _____ ☐ 12

3 Divide 848 sweets between four people. _____ ☐ 13

4 72 plants are arranged in groups of three. How many groups are there? _____ ☐ 14

5 How many horses can you shoe with 64 horseshoes? _____ ☐ 15

6 Divide 910 by 7. _____ ☐ 16

7 How many cars can have four new tyres if there are 768 tyres? _____ ☐ 17

Total test score

Score	1	2	3	4	5	6	7	8	9	10	11	12	13	14	15	16	17
%	6	12	18	24	29	35	41	47	53	59	65	71	76	82	88	94	100

☐ 17

Step 6: Three-digit ÷ one-digit first digit smaller than the divisor

In this step the first digit of the larger number is smaller than the divisor. Here notice that the first digit, 2, is less than the divisor 3.

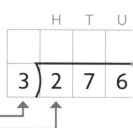

What to do

$276 \div 3 = ?$

1   Start in the same way with the hundreds digit, 2. Divide it by the divisor. Ask: *How many 3s in 2?* As there are **no** 3s in 2, write 0 above the line in the hundreds column and carry the 2. Write the 2 next to the tens digit, 7. Later, you won't need to write the zero – you can just leave a space there.

2   Then continue as normal with the tens. Instead of 7 we now have 27. Ask: *How many 3s in 27?* $27 \div 3 = 9$. Write the 9 in the tens column.

3   Then divide the units digit by the divisor, 3. Ask: *How many 3s in 6?* Write the 2 in the units column to complete the answer.

$$276 \div 3 = 92$$

Now you try

1
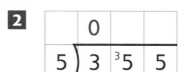

2
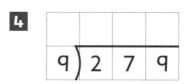

3

4

5
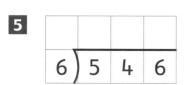

6
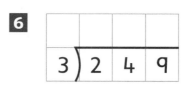

More practice

Set out these questions yourself to answer them.

7 426 ÷ 6 = ?

8 288 ÷ 4 = ?

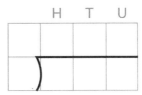

Problem solving

9 Look at this calculation. Can you see what error has been made?

$$5 \overline{\smash{)}\, 4\ 5\ 5} \quad \begin{matrix} 0 & 1 & 1 \end{matrix}$$

Error: _____

_____

Work out the correct answer.

$$5 \overline{\smash{)}\, 4\ 5\ 5} \qquad \underline{\quad}$$

10 Look at this calculation. Can you see what error has been made?

$$4 \overline{\smash{)}\, 2\ 8\ 4} \quad \begin{matrix} 2 & 2 & 1 \end{matrix}$$

Error: _____

_____

Work out the correct answer.

  _____

11 There are some cows in a field. If there are 368 legs, how many cows are there?

How did I find Step 6?   ☐ Easy   ☐ OK   ☐ Difficult

Step 7: Three-digit ÷ one-digit carrying tens

The questions in this step involve carrying once, but this time the carrying is from the tens to the units.

What to do

$876 ÷ 4 = ?$

1 Divide the hundreds digit by the divisor, 4. Ask: *How many 4s in 8?* Write the 2 above the line in the hundreds column.

	H	T	U
	2		
4⟌	8	7	6

2 Next look at the tens. Divide by the divisor, 4. Ask: *How many 4s in 7?* $7 ÷ 4 = 1$ r3. Write the 1 above the line in the tens column and carry the 3 to the units column.

		2	1	
4⟌	8	7	³6

3 Now look at the units digit. Instead of 6 we now have 36. Divide by the divisor, 4. Ask: *How many 4s in 36?* $36 ÷ 4 = 9$. Write the 9 in the units column to complete the answer.

		2	1	9
4⟌	8	7	³6

$876 ÷ 4 = 219$

Now you try

1

		3		
3⟌	9	8	²1

2

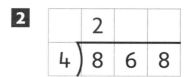

3

		1		
5⟌	5	8	5

4

6⟌	6	7	8

5

4⟌	4	9	6

6

3⟌	6	7	5

7

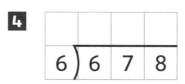

8

3⟌	3	8	1

More practice

Set out these questions yourself to answer them, including drawing the horizontal and vertical lines.

9 464 ÷ 4 = ? _____

```
 H   T   U
┌───┬───┬───┐
│   │   │   │
├───┼───┼───┤
│   │   │   │
└───┴───┴───┘
```

10 674 ÷ 2 = ? _____

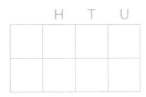

Problem solving

11 Four people win £872 on the lottery. They share it equally. How much does each person get?

_____

12 At the school there are 678 children. If all the children sit in groups of three, how many groups are there?

_____

13 A scientist has 678ml of liquid in a container. He pours exactly half into another container. How much liquid is in each container?

_____

14 Amit's father drives the same distance to work every day. If he drives 590km in five days, how far does he drive each day?

_____

15 A factory makes four-legged tables. How many tables can be made with 860 legs?

_____

How did I find Step 7?   ☐ Easy   ☐ OK   ☐ Difficult

Step 8: Three-digit ÷ one-digit second digit smaller than the divisor

In this step the second digit of the larger number is smaller than the divisor. Here notice that the second digit, 2, is less than the divisor, 3.

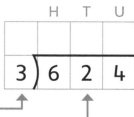

What to do

624 ÷ 3 = ?

1 Divide the hundreds digit by the divisor, 3. Ask: *How many 3s in 6?* Write the 2 above the line in the hundreds column.

H	T	U
	2	

3)6 2 4

2 Then look at the tens digit, 2. Ask: *How many 3s in 2?* As there are **no** 3s in 2, write 0 above the line in the tens column and write the carried 2 next to the units digit.

	2	0

3)6 2 ²4

3 Then continue as normal with the units. Instead of 4 we now have 24. Ask: *How many 3s in 24?* 24 ÷ 3 = 8. Write the 8 above the line to complete the answer.

	2	0	8

3)6 2 ²4

624 ÷ 3 = 208

Now you try

1

	3	0	
2)	6	1	¹6

2

		I		
5)	5	3	5

3

		2		
4)	8	2	8

4

9)	9	6	3

5

6)	6	3	6

6

More practice

Set out these questions yourself to answer them.

7 642 ÷ 6 = ?

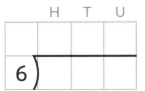

8 832 ÷ 4 = ?

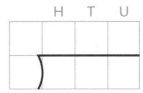

Problem solving

9 Look at this calculation. Can you see what error has been made?

```
      1 0 1
   4 ) 4 2 4
```

Error: _____

_____

What is the correct answer?

```
   4 ) 4 2 4          _____
```

10 Look at this calculation. Can you see what error has been made?

```
      1 4 2
   8 ) 8 2 4
```

Error: _____

_____

What is the correct answer?

_____

11 Which of these is the answer to 749 divided by 7?

17   11   101   107   170   190

_____

| How did I find Step 8? | ☐ Easy | ☐ OK | ☐ Difficult |

Step 9: Four-digit ÷ one-digit carrying once, any position

The questions in this step involve dividing four-digit numbers and carrying once, but you must decide when to carry. Also watch out for when a digit is smaller than the divisor, as you did in Step 8.

What to do

$9246 ÷ 3 = ?$

1 Divide the thousands digit by the divisor. Ask: *How many 3s in 9?* Write the answer in the thousands column.

Th	H	T	U
3			

3) 9 2 4 6

2 Divide the hundreds digit by the divisor. Ask: *How many 3s in 2?* As there are **no** 3s in 2, write 0 above it and write the carried 2 next to the tens digit.

| | 3 | 0 | | |

3) 9 2 ²4 6

3 Then look at the tens. Instead of 4 we now have 24. Ask: *How many 3s in 24?* $24 ÷ 3 = 8$. Write the 8 above the line.

| | 3 | 0 | 8 | |

3) 9 2 ²4 6

4 Finally divide the units digit by the divisor. $6 ÷ 3 = 2$. Write the 2 above the line to complete the answer.

| | 3 | 0 | 8 | 2 |

3) 9 2 ²4 6

Now you try

1

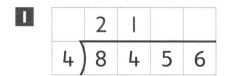

2

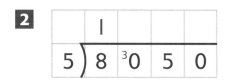

3

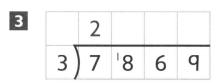

4

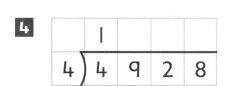

5

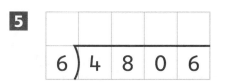

6

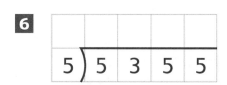

More practice

7

2)	6	8	5	6

8

7)	7	0	9	8

Set out these questions yourself to answer them.

9 5769 ÷ 3 = ?

Th	H	T	U
)			

10 8324 ÷ 4 = ?

Th	H	T	U
)			

Problem solving

11 How many weeks are 7735 days?

12 James has three times as much money as Paul has. If James has £6429, how much does Paul have?

13 Mrs Smith is four times as tall as her baby daughter. If Mrs Smith is 1684mm tall, how tall is her daughter?

14 A factory puts cereal bars into packs of six. How many packs can be made with 6306 bars?

How did I find Step 9?	☐ Easy	☐ OK	☐ Difficult

Check-up test 2 Three- and four-digit ÷ one-digit, carrying once

Step 6

 1

3⟍	2	4	3

2 426 ÷ 6 = ?

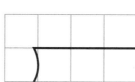

Step 7

3

6⟍	6	7	8

4 678 ÷ 3 = ?

Step 8

5

4⟍	8	2	8

6 927 ÷ 3 = ? _____

Step 9

7

3⟍	5	7	6	9

8 8324 ÷ 4 = ? _____

Steps 6 to 9 mixed

Use the grid below for working.

9 Share 216g of flour equally into three bowls.
How much flour is in each bowl? _____ ☐ 9

10 Three car parks can each hold the same number
of cars. They can take 981 cars altogether.
How many cars can park in each car park? _____ ☐ 10

11 Four people win £876 at the bingo. They share
it equally. How much does each person get? _____ ☐ 11

12 Divide 642 by 6. _____ ☐ 12

13 How many weeks is 7427 days? _____ ☐ 13

14 Jay has three times as much money saved as Sam has.
If Jay has £4539, how much does Sam have? _____ ☐ 14

Total test score

Score	1	2	3	4	5	6	7	8	9	10	11	12	13	14
%	7	14	21	29	36	43	50	57	64	71	79	86	93	100

14

Step 10: Three-digit ÷ one-digit carrying twice

Now you know how to carry once, you can carry twice!

What to do

$984 ÷ 4 = ?$

1 Divide the hundreds digit by the divisor, 4. Ask: *How many 4s in 9?* $9 ÷ 4 = 2$ r1. So write the 2 above the line in the hundreds column and carry the 1 next to the tens digit of the number.

	H	T	U
		2	
4)	9	¹8	4

2 Then look at the tens. Instead of 8 we now have 18. Divide by the divisor, 4. Ask: *How many 4s in 18?* $18 ÷ 4 = 4$ r2. Write the 4 above the line in the tens column and carry the 2 next to the units digit.

		2	4	
4)	9	¹8	²4	

3 Now look at the units digit. Instead of 4 we now have 24. Divide this by the divisor, 4. Ask: *How many 4s in 24?* Write the answer 6 in the units column.

		2	4	6
4)	9	¹8	²4	

Now you try

1

	3		
2)	7	¹3	8

2

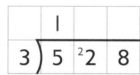

	1		
3)	5	²2	8

3

	1		
4)	7	4	4

4

5)	9	6	5

5

6)	8	1	6

6

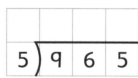

8)	3	6	8

7

7)	8	5	4

8

3)	8	6	4

More practice

 9

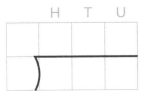

10

Set out these questions yourself to answer them.

11 885 ÷ 3 = ?

	H	T	U

12 952 ÷ 4 = ?

	H	T	U

Problem solving

13 635 ÷ 5 has the same answer as 508 ÷ 4. True or false?

_____

14 973 ÷ 7 has the same answer as 411 ÷ 3. True or false?

_____

15 A plank of wood is 474cm long. It is cut into three equal lengths. How long is each length?

_____

16 What is 456 shared equally between 8?

_____

17 Divide 888 by 6.

_____

How did I find Step 10? ☐ Easy ☐ OK ☐ Difficult

Step 11: Four-digit ÷ one-digit carrying two or three times

The questions here involve dividing four-digit numbers and carrying two or even three times, but you must decide when to carry.

What to do

$8736 \div 6 = ?$

1 Divide the thousands digit by the divisor. Ask: *How many 6s in 8?* $8 \div 6 = 1$ r2. Write the 1 above the line in the thousands column and carry the 2 to the hundreds column.

	Th	H	T	U
	1			
6)	8	²7	3	6

2 Now look at the hundreds. Instead of 7 we now have 27. Ask: *How many 6s in 27?* $27 \div 6 = 4$ r3. Write the 4 in the hundreds column and carry the 3 next to the tens digit.

		1	4	
6)	8	²7	³3	6

3 Next look at the tens. Instead of 3 we now have 33. Ask: *How many 6s in 33?* $33 \div 6 = 5$ r3. Write the 5 above and carry the 3.

		1	4	5
6)	8	²7	³3	³6

4 Then look at the units. Instead of 6 we now have 36. Divide 36 by 6. $36 \div 6 = 6$. Write the 6 above to complete the answer.

		1	4	5	6
6)	8	²7	³3	³6	

Now you try

1

	1	8		
4)	7	³4	5	6

2

		1		
5)	9	⁴0	7	0

3

	0			
8)	7	⁷8	4	8

4

		1		
3)	4	9	4	7

5

6)	7	9	0	8

6

4)	8	3	5	6

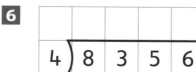

More practice

7

```
  |   |   |   |   |
2) 6 | 9 | 5 | 6
```

8

```
  |   |   |   |   |
7) 9 | 0 | 9 | 3
```

Set out these questions yourself to answer them.

9 8643 ÷ 3 = ?

Th	H	T	U
)			

10 7072 ÷ 4 = ?

Th	H	T	U
)			

Problem solving

11 There are three feet in a yard.
How many yards is 5280 feet?

12 Four people equally share £5748.
How much do they each get?

13 4528 people go to a football match.
If exactly one-eighth of the people
are children, how many children are
at the match?

14 Work out the missing number in
this calculation.

☐ × 5 = 4765

How did I find Step 11? Easy OK ☐ Difficult

Step 12: Three- or four-digit ÷ one-digit answers with remainders

So far all the divisions have resulted in whole number answers. But, if the large number is not a multiple of the divisor, the answer will **not** be a whole number. Here the answers have **remainders (r)**.

What to do

786 ÷ 5 = ?

1 As usual, working from the left, divide each digit by the divisor. For the hundreds digit ask: *How many 5s in 7?* 7 ÷ 5 = 1 r2. Write the 1 above and carry the 2.

	H	T	U
	1		
5)	7	²8	6

2 Next look at the tens. Instead of 8 we now have 28. Ask: *How many 5s in 28?* 28 ÷ 5 = 5 r3. Write the 5 above and carry the 3.

	1	5	
5)	7	²8	³6

3 Then look at the units. Instead of 6 we have 36. Divide 36 by 5. 36 ÷ 5 = 7 r1. Write 7 r1 above the line to complete the answer.

	1	5	7	r1
5)	7	²8	³6	

Now you try

1
```
      2       r
  4) 8 7 7
```

2
```
      1       r
  3) 4 7 2
```

3
```
      1       r
  6) 7 2 8
```

4
```
      1       r
  7) 7 1 7
```

5
```
  8) 9 8 3
```

6
```
  3) 9 7 7
```

More practice

Set out these questions yourself to answer them. These are all four-digit numbers.

7 $7777 \div 4 = ?$

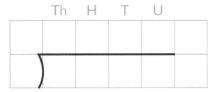

8 $9999 \div 7 = ?$

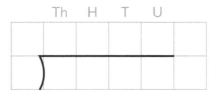

9 $3333 \div 5 = ?$

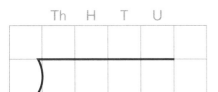

10 $8888 \div 3 = ?$

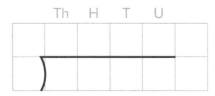

Problem solving

11 What is the remainder when 4245 is divided by 6?

r _____

12 A car factory has 5638 tyres in stock.
Four tyres are put on each car.
How many cars have four tyres and
how many tyres will be left over?

_____

_____

13 Work out the missing numbers in this calculation.

$4765 \div 8 =$ ☐ r ☐

| **How did I find Step 12?** | ☐ Easy | ☐ OK | ☐ Difficult |

Step 13: Five-digit ÷ one-digit answers with or without remainders

The questions here have five-digit numbers and some have answers with remainders.

What to do

$73\,229 \div 4 = ?$

1 As usual, work from the left and divide each digit by the divisor. For the first digit ask: *How many 4s in 7?* $7 \div 4 = 1\ r3$. Write the 1 above and carry the 3.

	TTh	Th	H	T	U
	1				
4)	7	³3	2	2	9

2 Then look at the next digit. Instead of 3 we now have 33. Ask: *How many 4s in 33?* $33 \div 4 = 8\ r1$. Write the 8 above and carry the 1.

	1	8			
4)	7	³3	¹2	2	9

3 Then look at the next digit. Instead of 2 we have 12. $12 \div 4 = 3$. Write the 3 above.

	1	8	3	0	
4)	7	³3	¹2	2	²9

4 For the next digit as there are **no** 4s in 2. Write 0 above and carry the 2.

5 Finally divide 29 by 4, which is 7 r1. Write this above the line to complete the answer.

	1	8	3	0	7	r1
4)	7	³3	¹2	2	²9	

Now you try

1

2
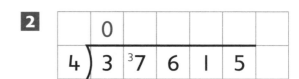

3
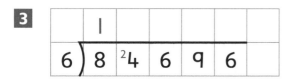

4

5
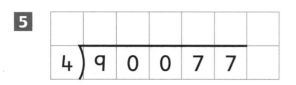

6
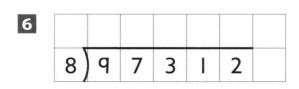

More practice

Set out these questions yourself to answer them, including drawing the horizontal and vertical lines.

7 $55\,555 \div 7 = ?$ _____

TTh	Th	H	T	U

8 $99\,999 \div 6 = ?$ _____

TTh	Th	H	T	U

9 $33\,333 \div 4 = ?$ _____

TTh	Th	H	T	U

10 $88\,888 \div 7 = ?$ _____

TTh	Th	H	T	U

Problem solving

11 How many weeks is 30 002 days?

_____

12 Work out the missing numbers in this calculation.

$53\,335 \div 4 = \boxed{} \ r \boxed{}$

13 Work out the missing numbers in this calculation.

$\boxed{} \times 6 = 29\,992 \ r \boxed{}$

How did I find Step 13?	☐ Easy	☐ OK	☐ Difficult

Check-up test 3 Three-, four- and five-digit ÷ one-digit, carrying more than once and remainders

Step 10

1

5⟌	9	6	5

2 952 ÷ 4 = ?

☐ 1
☐ 2

Step 11

3

3⟌	4	9	4	7

4 9075 ÷ 5 = ?

☐ 3
☐ 4

Step 12

Give your answers with remainders.

5

				r
6⟌	7	2	8	

6 6666 ÷ 7 = ?

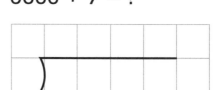

☐ 5
☐ 6

Step 13

7

6⟌	8	4	6	9	7

8 67 625 ÷ 6 = ?

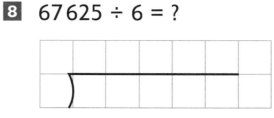

☐ 7
☐ 8

Steps 10 to 13 mixed

Use the grid below for working.

9 How many weeks is 20006 days?   _____   ☐ 9

10 Divide 5748 by 4.   _____   ☐ 10

11 A 477cm piece of rope is cut into three equal lengths.
How long is each length?   _____   ☐ 11

12 Divide 642 by 6.   _____   ☐ 12

13 What is the remainder when 4765 is divided by 8?   _____   ☐ 13

14 Find the missing numbers.

$37615 \div 4 = $ ☐ r ☐   ☐ 14

Total test score

Score	1	2	3	4	5	6	7	8	9	10	11	12	13	14
%	7	14	21	29	36	43	50	57	64	71	79	86	93	100

☐ 14

Step 14: Four-digit ÷ one-digit with fraction remainders

Sometimes when we divide, giving an answer with a remainder doesn't make sense. For example, *Pour 3685ml of water into three jars so that there is the same in each jar.* Having some water left over isn't an option. So your answer can't have a remainder.

3685ml ÷ 3

> ### What to do
>
> 3685 ÷ 3 = ?
>
> **1** Divide as before and work out what the remainder will be. Here 3685 ÷ 3 = 1228 r1.
>
> | | Th | H | T | U | |
> |---|---|---|---|---|---|
> | | | 1 | 2 | 2 | 8 | r1 |
> | 3) | 3 | 6 | 8 | ²5 | |
>
> **2** We can't give the answer with a remainder of 1. Dividing the remainder 1 by the divisor 3 gives you the fraction $\frac{1}{3}$ or one-third.
>
> | | | 1 | 2 | 2 | 8 | $\frac{1}{3}$ |
> |---|---|---|---|---|---|---|
> | 3) | 3 | 6 | 8 | ²5 | |
>
> **3** Notice that the numerator of the fraction (the number on top) is the remainder and the denominator (the number on the bottom) is the divisor.
>
> 3685ml ÷ 3 = $1228\frac{1}{3}$

Now you try

Give the remainder for each answer as a fraction.

1

	3			$\frac{}{2}$
2)	7	¹4	0	5	

2

	1			$\frac{}{4}$
4)	6	²4	0	7	

3

	1			
5)	8	3	7	3	

4

	0			
7)	6	5	8	4	

More practice

Give the remainder for each answer as a fraction.

5

6)	8	5	0	3	

6

9)	3	7	4	3	

Problem solving

Give the remainder for each answer as a fraction.

7 A school playground is 2745cm long. The teacher wants to split it into four equal lengths. How long would each length be?

_____

8 Mayya has 3547ml of juice for a party. She shares it equally between three large jugs. How much juice is in each jug?

_____

9 A factory makes wire. A length of wire that is 1138m long is cut into five equal lengths. How long is each length?

_____

10 Work out the missing digits in this calculation.

$5\ \square\ 7\ \square \div 8 = 658\ \frac{7}{\square}$

11 A 1648cm length of ribbon is cut into three equal lengths. How long is each length?

_____

How did I find Step 14?   ☐ Easy   ☐ OK   ☐ Difficult

Step 15: Four-digit ÷ one-digit with remainders as decimals, I dp

Sometimes it is more appropriate to give the remainder in an answer as a **decimal**. Using the same method of division, it is easy to find decimal answers. We use a decimal point and extra zero digits. Remember that 7324 is the same as 7324.0 (it just has a zero after the decimal point).

What to do

7324 ÷ 8 = ?

I As usual, divide each digit by the divisor.

	Th	H	T	U
	0	9	1	5

8) 7 ⁷3 ¹2 ⁴4

2 When you reach the end and would normally write the remainder, first put a decimal point at the end of the number and also above it in the answer. Next put a zero digit to the right of the number.

0 9 1 5 .

8) 7 ⁷3 ¹2 ⁴4 . 0

3 Then carry over the remainder. Here it is 4. Divide the digits after the decimal point by the divisor in the usual way. Ask: *How many 8s in 40?* Write the answer 5 above the line to complete the answer.

0 9 1 5 . 5

8) 7 ⁷3 ¹2 ⁴4 . ⁴0

7324 ÷ 8 = 915.5

Now you try

Give the remainder for each answer as a decimal.

I

4 7 7 3 .

2) 9 ⁵5 ¹4 7 . ¹0

2

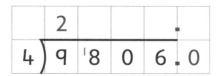

2

4) 9 ⁹8 0 6 . 0

3

1

5) 7 4 5 8 .

4

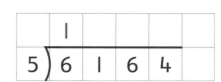

1

5) 6 1 6 4

5

4) 2 8 3 8

6

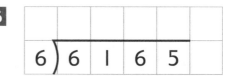

6) 6 1 6 5

More practice   Set out these questions yourself to answer them.

Give the remainder for each answer as a decimal.

7   5636 ÷ 8 = ?

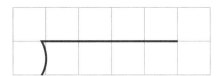

8   9561 ÷ 5 = ?

9   2147 ÷ 5 = ?

10   8835 ÷ 6 = ?

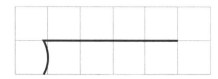

Problem solving

Give the remainder for each answer as a decimal.

11   A building company makes four identical deliveries of bricks. The total weight of the bricks was 5258kg. How heavy was each delivery?

12   A scientist measures 1773ml of acid. She pours it equally into five measuring jugs. How much does she put into each jug?

13   Eight people win a joint prize. They share the prize of £4860 equally between them. How much does each get?

14   Mr Coin gives the same amount of money to each of his five daughters. He gives them £1751 in total. How much is each daughter given?

How did I find Step 15?   ☐ Easy   ☐ OK   ☐ Difficult

Step 16: Four-digit ÷ one-digit with remainders as decimals, 2 or 3 dp

Here the answers will have 2 or 3 decimal places. Remember that 1146 is the same as 1146.00 or 1146.000. You can keep writing zeros after the decimal point without changing the number!

What to do

$1146 \div 8 = ?$

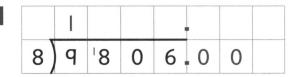

1 As usual, divide each digit by the divisor.

2 When you reach the end and would normally write a remainder, first put a decimal point at the end of the number and also above it in the answer. Then put two zeros to the right of the number.

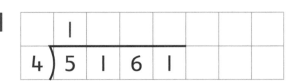

3 Now carry over the remainder. Here it is 2. Divide the digits after the decimal point by the divisor in the usual way, carrying as necessary. Ask: *How many 8s in 20?* Write 2 above and carry 4.

4 Finally divide 40 by 8 and write 5 above to complete the answer.

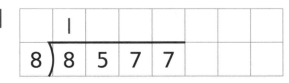

$1146 \div 8 = 143.25$

Now you try

Give the remainder for each answer as a decimal.

1

```
      2  3  8  6 .
  4) 9 ¹5 ³4 ²7.³0  0
```

2

```
         1            .
  8) 9 ¹8  0  6.0  0
```

3

```
      0              .
  8) 7  4  1  8 .
```

4

```
      1
  4) 5  1  6  1
```

5

```
      0
  8) 1  5  7  1
```

6

```
      1
  8) 8  5  7  7
```

More practice   Set out these questions yourself to answer them.

Give the remainder for each answer as a decimal.

7 7637 ÷ 4 = ?

8 9561 ÷ 8 = ?

Problem solving   Give the remainder for each answer as a decimal.

9 When 4637 is divided by 4 the answer is 1159.45. True or false?

10 When any **odd** number is divided by 4 the answer will end in .25 or .75. True or false?

11 If eight people share £5862 equally they will each get £732.75. True or false?

12 Repeat a digit four times to create a four-digit number, for example 3333. Divide it by 8. Using spare paper, do the same for each digit from 1 to 9, dividing by 8 each time. Look for patterns in the last digits of the answers. Which questions give you answers with one digit after the decimal point, which give you two digits after the decimal point, which give you three digits after the decimal point or which give you whole number answers?

How did I find Step 16?   ☐ Easy   ☐ OK   ☐ Difficult

Step 17: Three-digit ÷ one-digit with remainders as recurring decimals

Not every remainder can be written as a decimal with one, two or three digits after the decimal point. Some decimals keep on going forever. They are called **recurring decimals**. You'll see why this happens in this example.

$473 \div 3 = ?$

What to do

1 Divide each digit by the divisor.

	H	T	U		
	1	5	7		
3 ⟌	4	¹7	²3		

2 When you reach the end and would normally write a remainder, put a decimal point at the end of the number and also above it in the answer. Put zeros to the right of the number.

	1	5	7 .			
3 ⟌	4	¹7	²3 .	0	0	0

3 Now carry over the remainder. Here it is 2. Divide the digits after the decimal point by the divisor in the usual way, carrying as necessary. Ask: *How many 3s in 20?* Write 6 above and carry 2.

	1	5	7 . 6			
3 ⟌	4	¹7	²3 .	²0	²0	0

4 Keep going, but each time you will see that we write 6 above and carry the 2. You could keep going forever! This is a recurring decimal. We write a dot over the last digit to show that it is recurring.

	1	5	7 . 6	6	6	
3 ⟌	4	¹7	²3 .	²0	²0	²0

$473 \div 3 = 157.\dot{6}$

Now you try

Write the answers on the lines below.

1

	1	1	.				
3 ⟌	3	5	²2 .	0	0	0	0

$352 \div 3 = $ _____

2

	0		.			
9 ⟌	4	⁴8	1 .			

$481 \div 9 = $ _____

More practice   Write the answers on the lines below.

1

		0	4				
6	)	2	²7	³2			

272 ÷ 6 = _____

4

			1				
9	)	9	7	4			

974 ÷ 9 = _____

3

3	)	1	9	1			

191 ÷ 3 = _____

6

9	)	4	7	6			

476 ÷ 9 = _____

Problem solving

7   Which of these divisions gives a recurring decimal answer?

573 ÷ 3   573 ÷ 6   573 ÷ 4   573 ÷ 9

_____

8   Which digit recurs in the question
888 ÷ 9?

_____

9   Kim divides 457 by 3. Which three of
the answers below are correct answers
to 457 ÷ 3? Circle them.

152 r1 $152\frac{1}{2}$ 152   152.3

152.1   152.$\dot{3}$ $152\frac{1}{3}$

How did I find Step 17?	Easy	OK	Difficult

Step 18: Dividing decimals by one-digit numbers

Now that you know how to divide whole numbers by one-digit numbers you can divide decimals in the same way. Just follow the same method and make sure you put the decimal point in the correct place in the answer.

What to do

$7.32 \div 8 = ?$

1 Write a decimal point in the answer directly above the decimal point in the number.

```
        U . t   h
      .
  8) 7 . 3  2
```

2 As usual, divide each digit by the divisor.

```
     0 . 9  1
  8) 7 .⁷3 ¹2
```

3 If necessary, write zeros at the end of the number to help you complete the answer. You can do this because 7.32 is the same as 7.320 or 7.3200.

```
     0 . 9  1
  8) 7 .⁷3 ¹2  0
```

4 Now carry over the remainder. Here it is 4. Divide 40 by 8 to complete the answer.

```
     0 . 9  1  5
  8) 7 .⁷3 ¹2 ⁴0
```

$7.32 \div 8 = 0.915$

Now you try

1
```
     4 .
  2) 9 .¹5  4
```

2
```
     2 .
  4) 9 .¹8  0
```

3
```
     0 .
  5) 2 . 4  8
```

4
```
  5) 6 . 1  6
```

5
```
  8) 3 . 4  2
```

6
```
  6) 6 . 1  5
```

More practice

Set out these questions yourself to answer them. Write the answers on the lines.

7 $5.63 \div 8 = ?$

$5.63 \div 8 =$ _____

8 $9.61 \div 5 = ?$

$9.61 \div 5 =$ _____

Problem solving

9   What is £9.15 shared equally between five friends?

_____

10   A scientist has 1.78kg of crystals, which he puts into eight equal piles. How heavy is each pile?

_____

11   A nurse must measure one-fifth of a dose of medicine to give to a child. If the full dose is 9.84ml, how much should be given to the child?

_____

12   A length of wood that is 2.72m long is cut into four equal pieces. How long is each piece in metres?

_____

13   Divide 3.04 by 8.

_____

How did I find Step 18?   ☐ Easy   ☐ OK   ☐ Difficult

Final test Whole numbers or decimals ÷ one-digit, with remainders

Step 14

Give the remainder for each answer as a fraction.

1

$$4\overline{)6\ 4\ 0\ 7}$$

2 $3743 \div 9 = ?$

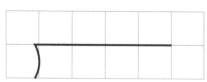

Steps 15 and 16

Give your answers as decimals.

3

$$5\overline{)2\ 1\ 4\ 7}$$

4 $2977 \div 8 = ?$

Step 17

Give your answers as recurring decimals.

5

$$3\overline{)5\ 7\ 4}$$

$574 \div 3 =$ _____

6

$$9\overline{)9\ 7\ 4}$$

$974 \div 9 =$ _____

Step 18

Give your answers as decimals.

7

$$5\overline{)7.4\ 9}$$

8 $5.7 \div 8 = ?$

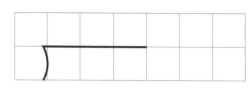

Steps 1 to 18 mixed

Use the grid below for working.

9 How many cars can have four new tyres if there are 876 tyres? _____ ☐ 9

10 762 ÷ 6 has the same answer as 381 ÷ 3. True or false? _____ ☐ 10

11 Jay has five times as much money as Lin has. If Jay has £8485, how much does Lin have? _____ ☐ 11

12 A factory puts cakes into packs of six. How many packs are made with 6306 cakes? _____ ☐ 12

13 Divide 885 by 3. _____ ☐ 13

14 There are three feet in a yard. How many yards is 4782 feet? _____ ☐ 14

15 £4766 is shared equally between eight friends. How much does each get? _____ ☐ 15

16 Divide 3525 by 6 and give the remainder both as a fraction and as a decimal. _____ ☐ 16

Total test score

Score	1	2	3	4	5	6	7	8	9	10	11	12	13	14	15	16
%	6	13	19	25	31	38	44	50	56	63	69	75	81	88	94	100

16

Schofield & Sims

FOR THE NEW
NATIONAL
CURRICULUM

the long-established educational publisher specialising in maths, English and science

Written Calculation comprises six **Pupil Books**, six **Answer Books**, a **Teacher's Guide** and a **Teacher's Resource Book** and uses methods recommended in the National Curriculum. Designed for use at Key Stage 2, each **Pupil Book** uses 18 carefully structured steps to guide the learner towards full mastery of each written method, supporting them in their national tests and other areas of the National Curriculum. **Written Calculation** also helps pupils develop confidence and fluency in their learning by practising and embedding place value, number facts and problem solving skills. The importance of estimating and checking answers is also emphasised.

Written Calculation: Division 1 leads pupils through the necessary steps for mastering short division. Pupils beginning this book should have an understanding of the value of digits in two- and three-digit numbers and experience of multiplying and dividing small numbers. Pupils who have learnt their times tables and related division facts will find written division easier.

Each of the 18 steps features the following sections.
- *What to do* – detailed explanations and a worked example.
- *Now you try* – questions that are similar to those in the worked example.
- *More practice* – questions that are more difficult and provide less support than those in *Now you try*.
- *Problem solving* – word problems.
- *Self-evaluation rating* – to help identify pupils who may be struggling with the step.

Three *Check-up tests* and a *Final test* enable you to monitor pupils' progress and quickly convert scores to percentages. These scores may later be recorded on the *Group record sheet*.

The accompanying **Teacher's Guide** provides useful notes and ideas for planning lessons, enabling a whole-school approach. Detailed *Teaching notes* outline clear learning objectives and a *Summary of the steps* for each **Pupil Book** is included. Photocopiable *Assessment resources* allow you to monitor and assess pupils' progress.

Supplementary *Further practice* and *Problem solving questions* can be found in the **Teacher's Resource Book**. These photocopiable resources may be used for further practice, assessment, revision or homework and correspond to the steps covered in each of the **Pupil Books**.

The full range of books in the series is as follows.

Addition	978 0 7217 1266 6	**Addition Answers**	978 0 7217 1272 7
Subtraction	978 0 7217 1267 3	**Subtraction Answers**	978 0 7217 1273 4
Multiplication 1	978 0 7217 1268 0	**Multiplication 1 Answers**	978 0 7217 1274 1
Multiplication 2	978 0 7217 1269 7	**Multiplication 2 Answers**	978 0 7217 1275 8
Division 1	978 0 7217 1270 3	**Division 1 Answers**	978 0 7217 1276 5
Division 2	978 0 7217 1271 0	**Division 2 Answers**	978 0 7217 1277 2
Teacher's Guide	978 0 7217 1278 9	**Teacher's Resource Book**	978 0 7217 1300 7

Free downloads, available from the **Written Calculation** page of the Schofield & Sims website, enhance the effectiveness of the series. These are updated as necessary to ensure that **Schofield & Sims Written Calculation** meets the requirements of the National Curriculum.

MIX
Paper from
responsible sources
FSC® C010219

ISBN 978-07217-1270-3

9 780721 712703

ISBN 978 0 7217 1270 3
Key Stage 2
Age range from 7 years
£3.50
(Retail price)